HERO ACTIVITIES

MARVEL
marvel.com

Bath • New York • Cologne • Melbourne • Delhi
Hong Kong • Shenzhen • Singapore

This edition published by Parragon Books Ltd in 2016

Parragon Books Ltd
Chartist House
15–17 Trim Street
Bath BA1 1HA, UK
www.parragon.com

MARVEL

ISBN 978-1-4748-3246-5

Printed in China

AVENGERS ASSEMBLE!

Earth's Mightiest Heroes will face any threat together.
Can you spot five things that are different in the bottom picture?
Circle them all.

Answers on page 31

ANOTHER ULTRON

Tony Stark and Dr Bruce Banner created the artifici intelligence Ultron to defer humanity. But it has gone beyond its programming and wants to destroy all life on Earth!

Use the grid below to copy the picture of this dangerous machine, then colour in your drawing.

COLOUR FOR CAP

Captain America fights for truth and justice. Colour in this picture of the First Avenger!

ANGRY AVENGER

Dr Bruce Banner becomes the Hulk when he's angry! Colour in this picture of the Incredible Avenger.

AMAZING MAZE

Black Widow needs to find her Avengers teammates – can you help her through the maze?

START

FINISH

Answers on page 31

WEAPON OF A GOD

Join the dots to reveal Thor's mighty weapon.

24 1 2

22 23 3 4

21 5

20 6

19 7

18 17 9 8

16 10

15 11

14 13 12

SUPER SCRAMBLE

What sort of being is Ultron? Cross out every second letter in the circle, then write down the letters that are left to reveal the answer. The first letter of each word has been done for you.

START

A _ _ _ _ _ _ _ _ _

I _ _ _ _ _ _ _ _ _ _ _

Answer on page 31

PUZZLE PIECES

The Avengers are flying into the final battle with Ultron. Thor is summoning lightning and Iron Man is preparing a repulsor blast....
Draw a line to show where each missing piece of the picture fits.

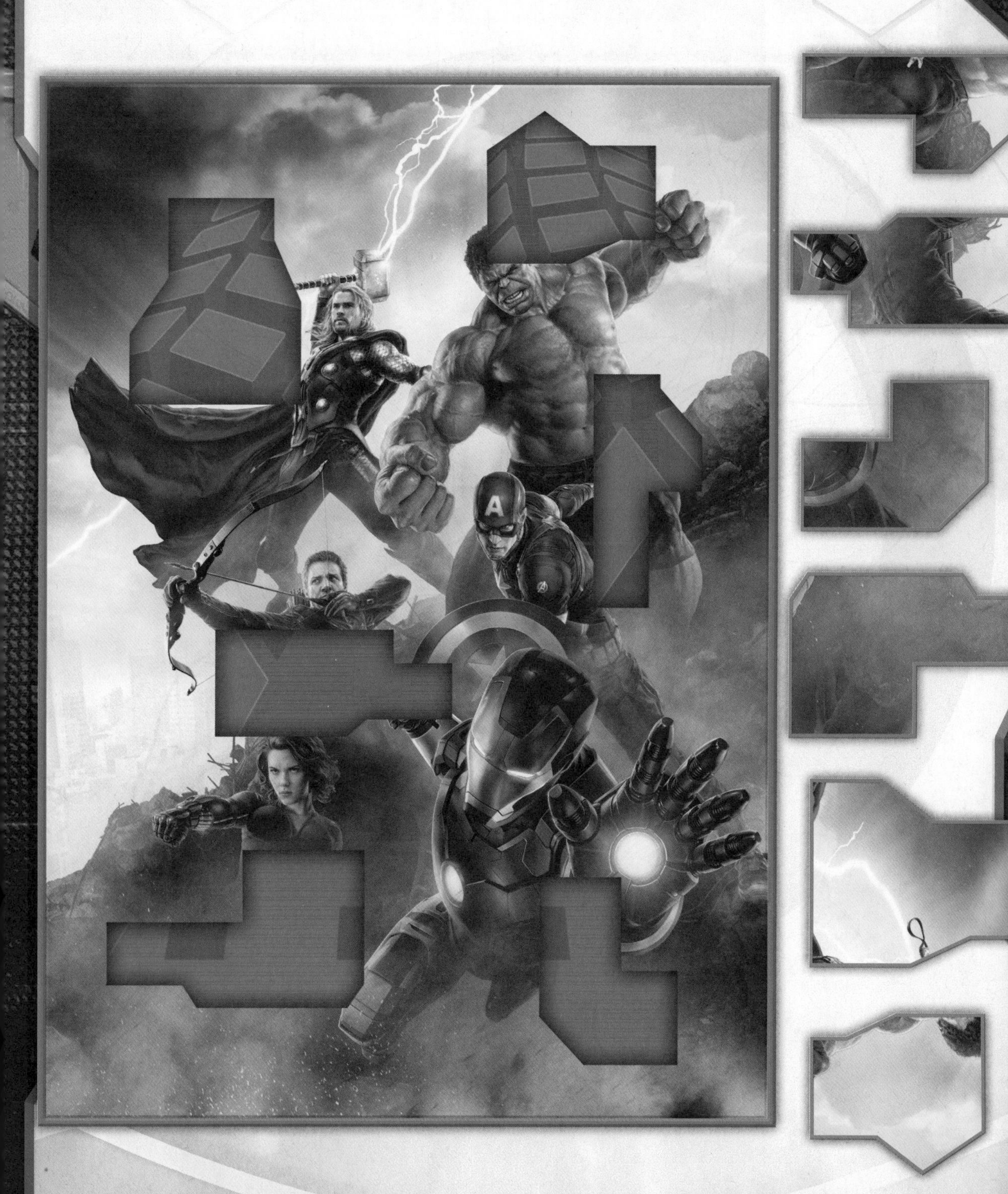

Answers on page 31

DOUBLE VISION

The Vision was programmed by Tony Stark and Bruce Banner to help the Avengers. He can fly and fire energy beams!

Spot five differences between the two pictures, then colour in this avenging ally.

BLURRED BATTLE

Missiles, explosions and lightning bolts create a lot of smoke and dust. Can you tell who's who in all the confusion? Draw lines to connect the names to the correct characters.

Be careful!

Not everyone in there is a friend!

HAWKEYE ULTRON BLACK WIDOW

HULK IRON MAN VISION

Answer on page 31

SHADOWY AGENT

Only one of these shadows exactly matches Black Widow.
Can you find it?

ANSWER:

Answers on page 31

CAPTAIN CONFUSION

Steve Rogers became Captain America when he was blasted with Vita-Rays and given a special serum. Find the two matching pictures of Captain America and circle them.

Answer on page 31

SPOT THE DIFFERENCE

Find six things that are different between these two shadowy images of the Avengers.

ACCURATE ARROWS

The Avengers need every one of Hawkeye's high-tech arrows to hit its target if they are to defeat Ultron. Which line scores a direct hit on Ultron?

Answer on page 32

SUPER MEMORY POWERS

Do you have a genius mind like Bruce Banner? Look at this picture of the Avengers for 20 seconds, then cover it up and answer the questions below to find out!

1) Which building is in the background?
- Empire State Building
- Chrysler Building
- Avengers Tower

2) What kind of weapon is Black Widow holding?
- Gun
- Baton
- Missile launcher

3) What letter does Captain America have on his helmet?
- A - C - P

4) What is Thor surrounded by?
- Rain
- Robots
- Lightning

5) Including Vision, how many Avengers are in the picture?
- 7 - 6 - 8

TRUE OR FALSE?

How much do you know about the Avengers and their battle with Ultron? Decide if each of these statements is true or false, then check your answers on page 48.

1 Ultron is a human being.

TRUE  FALSE

2 Thor's mighty hammer is called 'Asgard'.

TRUE  FALSE

3 Black Widow was born and trained in Russia.

TRUE  FALSE

4 The Avengers' headquarters, Avengers Tower, is in London.

TRUE  FALSE 

Answer on page 32

5 Captain America's shield is made of Vibranium.

TRUE ◯ **FALSE** ◯

6 Vision can see through walls.

TRUE ◯ **FALSE** ◯

7 Dr Bruce Banner turns into the Hulk when he's happy.

TRUE ◯ **FALSE** ◯

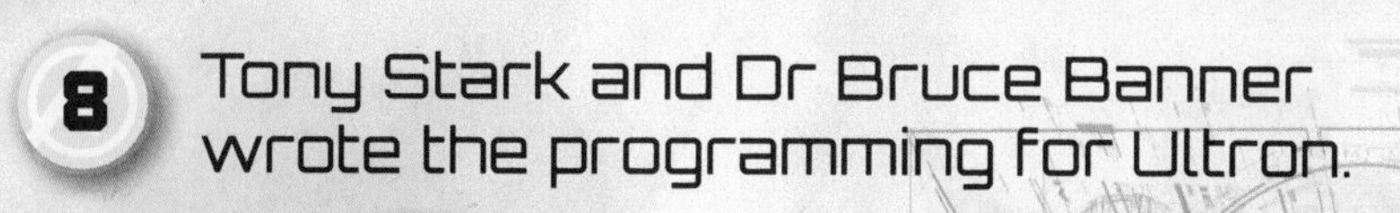

8 Tony Stark and Dr Bruce Banner wrote the programming for Ultron.

TRUE ◯ **FALSE** ◯

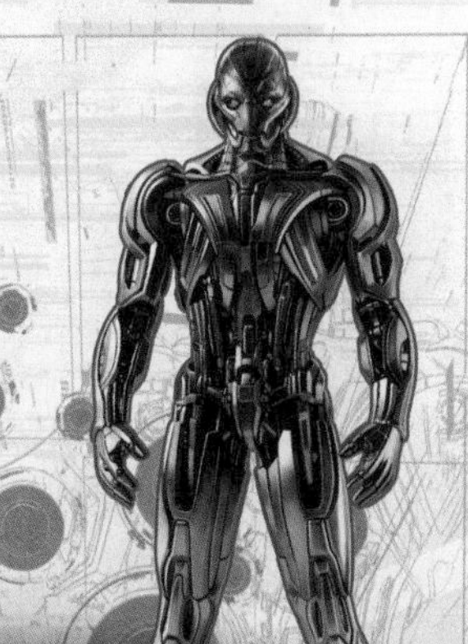

Answers on page 32

IRON MAN MESS

Draw lines to put the pieces of Iron Man's picture in the right places.

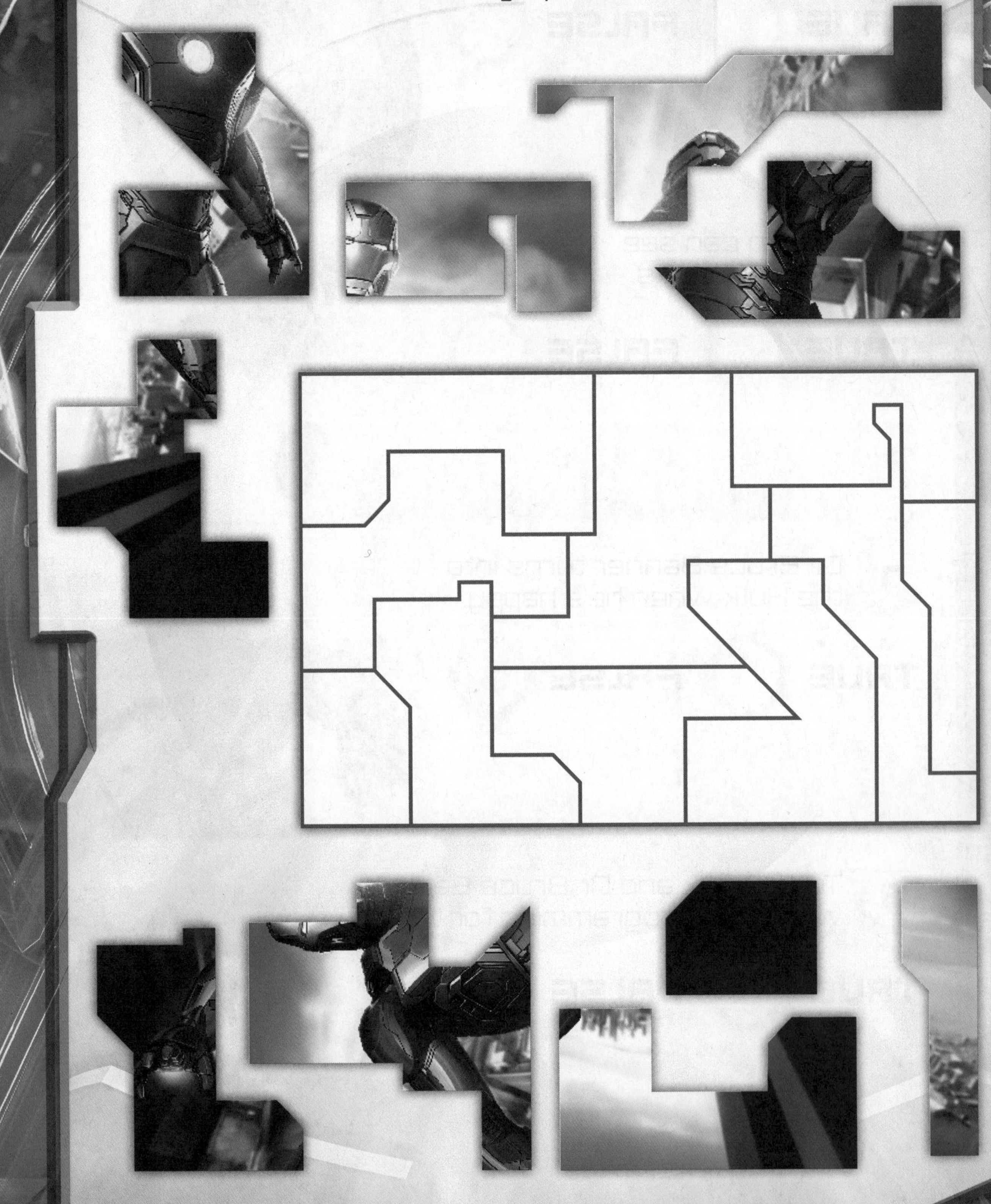

Answer on page 32

BUST THE HULK

Tony Stark knows that the Hulk can get out of control sometimes – so he builds the Hulkbuster robot to keep him in check.
Design your own powerful robot to take on the Hulk!

What great high-tech features and weapons would your robot have?

....

....

The Avengers can't defeat Ultron until they find him! Guide them through the maze so they can take down the crazed computer.

Finish

Answer on page 32

SUPER SPEED

Captain America can run incredibly fast, and he's rushing to battle Ultron! Work out how long each path would take him by adding up the seconds along the way.

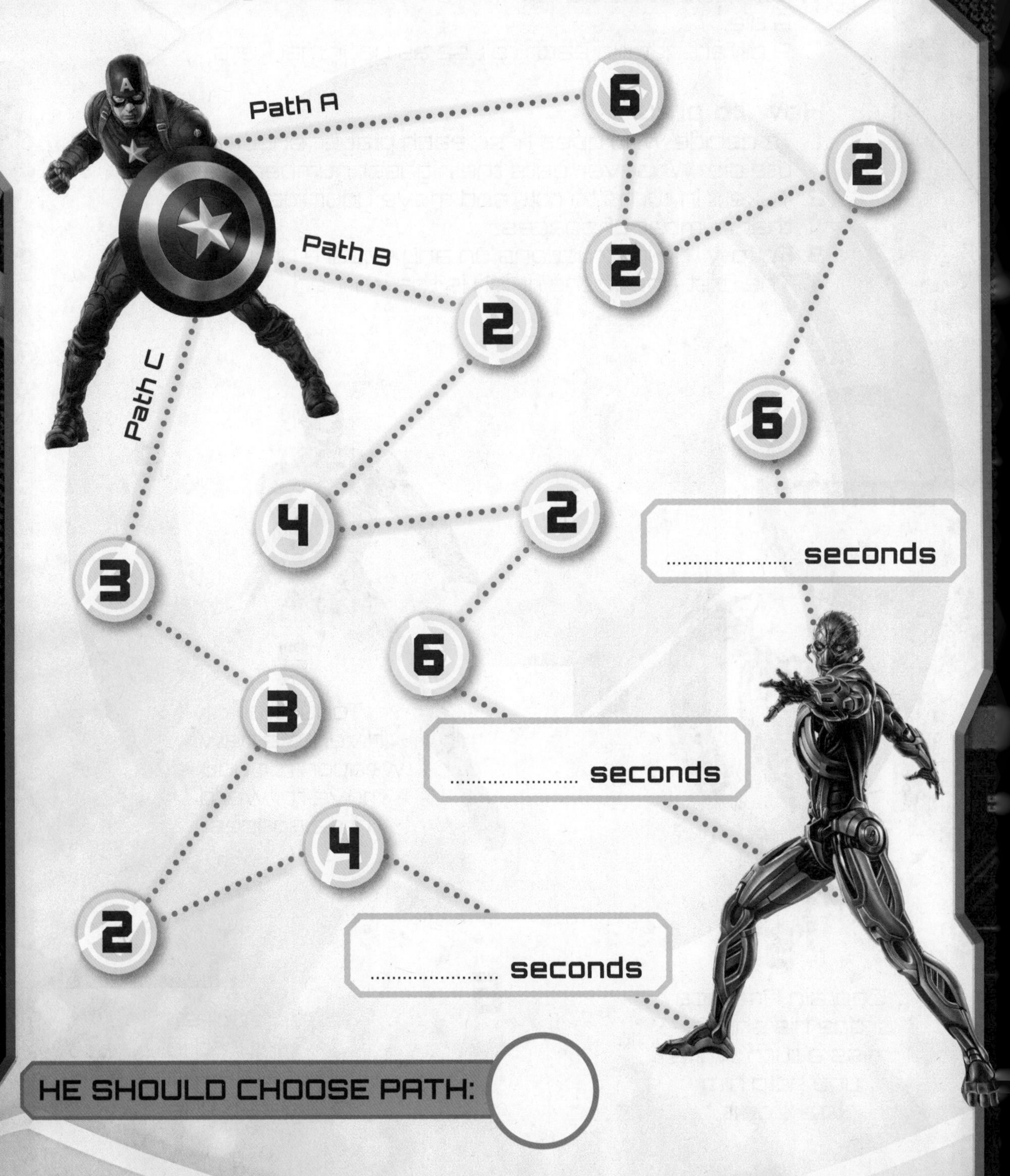

HE SHOULD CHOOSE PATH:

Answers on page 32

GAME OF HEROES

Play this game with at least one friend.

What you'll need

- A die.
- A different coin each to use as your markers.

How to play

1. To decide who goes first, each player should roll the die. Whoever gets the highest number goes first.
2. Take it in turns to roll, and move your markers that number of spaces.
3. Follow the instructions on any square you land on.
4. The first one to the finish is the winner!

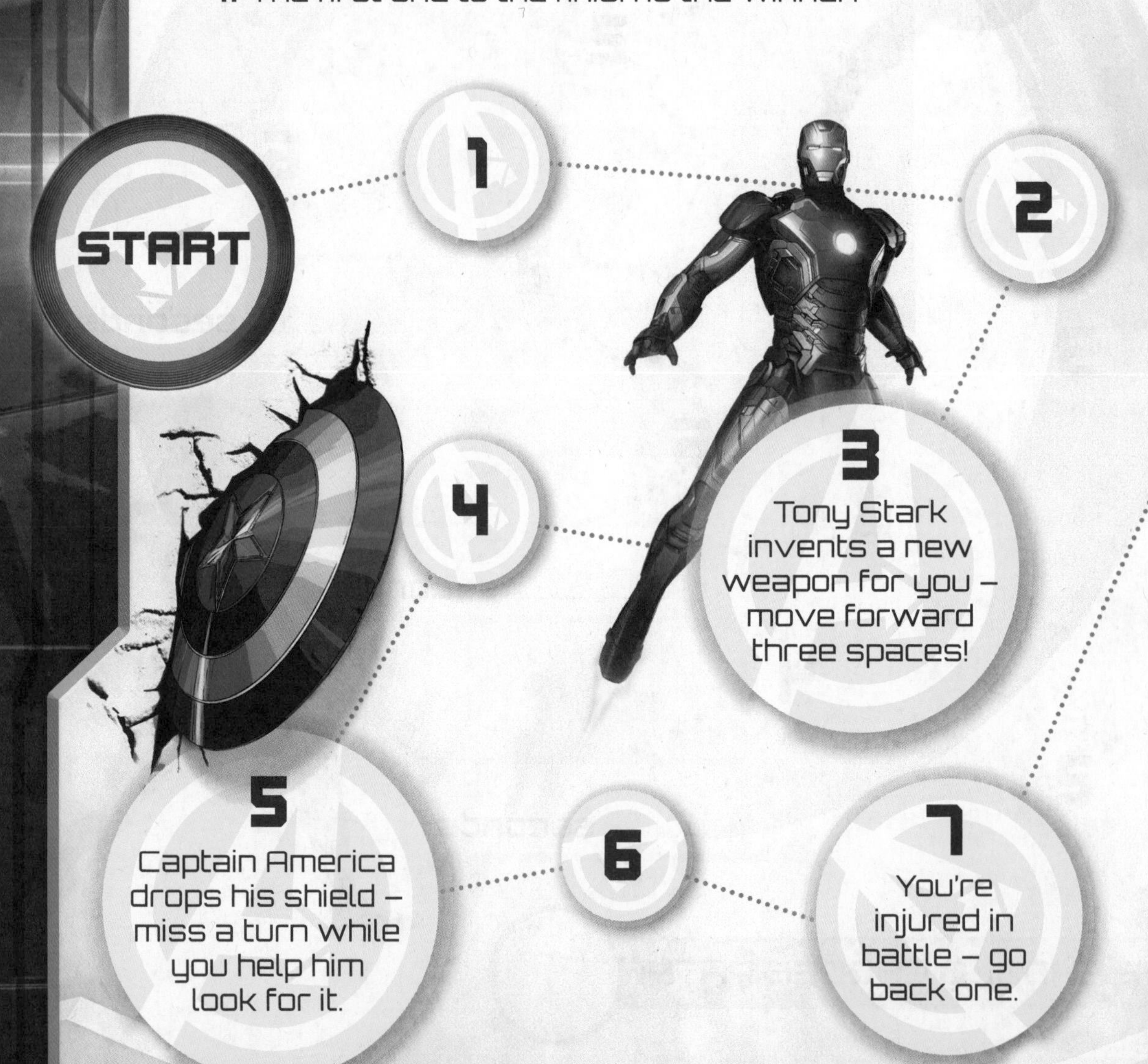

START
1
2
3
Tony Stark invents a new weapon for you – move forward three spaces!
4
5
Captain America drops his shield – miss a turn while you help him look for it.
6
7
You're injured in battle – go back one.

8
9
10
The Hulk loses control! Miss a turn while you stop to calm him down.
11
12
13
14
15
Vision comes to your aid – go forward three spaces.
16
Ultron has sensed your movements – go back to number 6.
17
18
19
20
21
Ultron attacks! You must roll a 2 to leave this square and finish.
22
FINISH

CODE CRACKING

Black Widow uses a lot of spy codes. Can you use the key to read the message she's left for the other Avengers?

KEY

A	B	C	D	E	F	G	H	I	J	K	L	M
26	25	24	23	22	21	20	19	18	17	16	15	14

N	O	P	Q	R	S	T	U	V	W	X	Y	Z
13	12	11	10	9	8	7	6	5	4	3	2	1

MESSAGE

6 15 7 9 12 13 ' 8

18 13

14 26 13 19 26 7 7 26 13

_ _ _ _ _ _ ' _

_ _

_ _ _ _ _ _ _ _ _

Answer on page 32

DARING DOOR-HANGER

Ask an adult to help you cut around the dotted lines, then hang this on your door handle to let everyone know if you need a teammate, or if they need to stay away!

KEEP OUT!
BATTLE IN PROGRESS!

COME IN -
MORE AVENGERS NEEDED!

ANSWERS

Page 3

Page 8

Page 10
ARTIFICIAL INTELLIGENCE

Page 11

Pages 12–13

Page 14

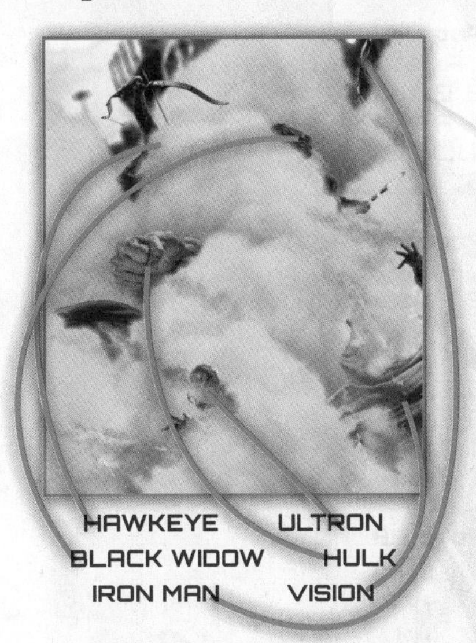

Page 15
Shadow C

Page 16

Page 17

ANSWERS

Page 18
Arrow 2

Page 19
1. Avengers Tower
2. Baton
3. A
4. Lightning
5. 7

Pages 20-21
1. False
2. False
3. True
4. False
5. True
6. False
7. False
8. True

Page 22

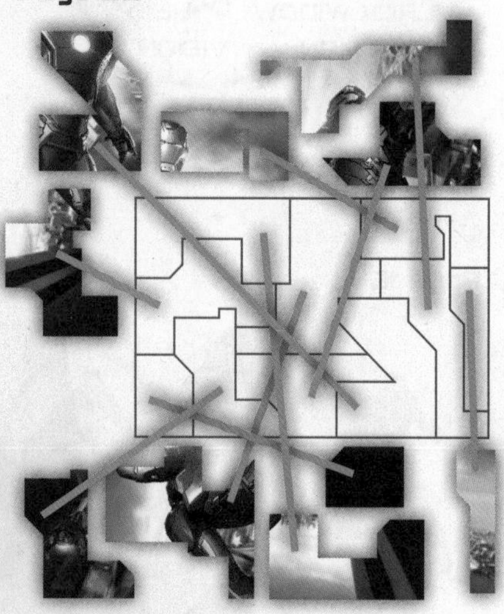

Page 24

Page 25
Path A: 16 seconds
Path B: 14 seconds
Path C: 12 seconds

He should choose path C

Page 28
ULTRON'S IN MANHATTAN